PATTERNS OF LIFE

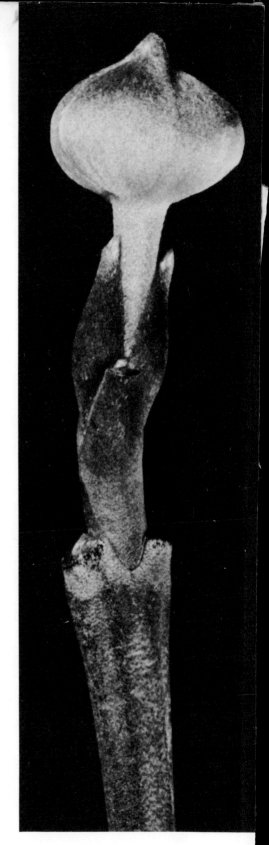

*The
Unseen
World
of
Plants*

PATTERNS
OF
LIFE

WILLIAM M. HARLOW

*Prologue by
Paul B. Sears*

*Harper & Row, Publishers
New York*

The reproductions of
the male flowering cones
of jack pine, sugar maple and willow flowers
first appeared in
Textbook of Dendrology by W. M. Harlow
and E. S. Harrar,
McGraw-Hill Book Co., 1958

FIRST EDITION

Library of Congress Catalog Card Number: 66–13918
Designed by The Etheredges
Lithographed by
The Murray Printing Company
Forge Village, Massachusetts

To Alma, My Wife

CONTENTS

7

PROLOGUE

At least three hundred million years have elapsed since plant life emerged from its cradle in the sea and began to adjust to life upon the land. No longer could the nutrient bath of sea water be relied upon; instead the plant was now required to extract for itself carbon from the air, to draw moisture and minerals from the earth, and to reach for its proper share of life-giving energy from the sun.

In order to survive, the adventuring plants were also obliged to develop a kind of protection from the new changes which surrounded them —transitions of light, moisture, and temperature from day to night and season to season. Only the fossil imprints which chanced to form—and the much smaller number which have been found—tell of this past. Yet few as they are they give evidence of the steady catalogue of change, the trials and errors which give diversity to the planet and man's struggle to stay alive.

As to the earliest stages of evolution, we must be content with what we find. About us, though, at the present moment, there is ample testimony to the successful adaptation of life to the land. We need only learn to *see,* and nowhere is there more of beauty and variety than in these heralds of ourselves, the kingdom of living plants. Despite our most ingenious efforts these remain indispensable to our delight and to our survival. For that matter, our pleasure may be directly responsible for the preservation of the evidence, for we are not likely to save what we have not learned to enjoy.

However close their resemblances, two plants, or even two leaves on the same stem, are never alike. Behind these differences in detail, however, there are degrees of likenesses, sufficient to enable the plant kingdom to be ordered into divisions and lesser hierarchies. All told, some third of a million species of plants are known, or more, and many are yet to be discovered, classified, and named. This naming is a mixture of science and art, truth often passing from beauty to eye to brain.

The greater man's desire to know and order his world, the greater his refinement in naming it. This need not discourage the amateur, however, for he can be content with something less than exact scientific orderings, as must those who pursue the exact sciences at times. More to the point for us are a few simple facts about those kinds of plants—less than half of the kingdom—which give character to our familiar surroundings: the larger land plants—the trees, shrubs, and herbs. Except for the ferns, which retain an ancient mode of reproduction, these rooted plants form seeds and have within their bodies supporting strands which also serve as pathways along which raw materials and food can be moved.

A great variety of these root systems exists to meet the contingencies of life on land. By means of them, the plant is anchored in the soil which sustains it, at the same time storing food and avoiding obstacles and searching for water and nutrients as surely as a pointer scents a hidden partridge. They are adaptable to their surroundings as well, the root systems of most desert plants spreading horizontally close to the soil surface in order to trap the shallow moisture from infrequent rains, the closely packed roots of marsh and prairie plants absorbing at different levels, all according to their kind. More than many realize, the conditions of life on earth depend to a great extent on what happens in the lightless recesses of the soil.

Our concern here is mainly with the shoot, however, easily visible to all who have lacked the curiosity or energy to dig and examine root systems. The photographs which follow show, through their great variety, how the shoot, like a symphony, is based on but a single theme: the geometry of the spiral. Exposed to light and air, and needing both, the shoot must at the same time be prepared to meet the hazards of a changeable atmosphere. From the shoot comes the leaf, its various silhouettes and thicknesses necessary to receive the plant's radiant energy from the sun and carbon dioxide from the air. Within its green cells, the carbon combines with water and minerals which have been supplied by the roots, enabling the leaf, through the chemical process of photosynthesis, to release the oxygen needed by other life forms. Beneath the waxy coating of the leaf which is supplied with tiny pores which can open and close to minimize evaporation, are the soft tissues braced by veins of fiber and tubules for the transport of dissolved minerals and foods. These veins, running as parallel strands in grasses and lilies and their kin, form the delicate networks in other flowering plants as well.

The shoot begins as a growing point in which the future panoply of the leafy stem is laid down. As the point develops, the leaves expand—in rosette plants such as the dandelion, the spiral remains closely packed; in most plants each leaf or pair of opposite leaves is carried upward by the growth of the segment of stem which separates it from the next older layer, thus elongating or opening the spiral. A young head of cabbage shows the fundamental plan very well since each new leaf develops just above and to the side of its predecessor, like steps on a winding staircase.

This plan is an extremely effective one, operating to give each leaf its just share of light and space, the green shoots tending to grow toward the light if shaded, thus furthering the effectiveness of the original spiral. Just above the junction of leaf and stem is a bud, a tiny nascent shoot with its delicate growing tissues shielded from dryness and cold by a protective scaling. Just as the leaf's form expresses characteristics of the different species, so do the details of bud form and outer texture speak of the nature of the growing point, the development of which produces a new leafy branch. Plants which do not branch, such as the palm, manage to survive by virtue of a great single bud at their tip that supplies a tight spiral of new leaves as the older leaves below die away. Unlike the branching plants, their stems need not thicken with age in order to bear the growing weight of an increasingly heavy crown, and growth rings found in other trees do not develop.

In order that they may perpetuate their kind, seed-bearing plants have developed compact shoots, the flowers of which are modified leaves. The most primitive flower-type is the regular spiral of the cone, and from that repetitive simplicity of similar parts, the flower has evolved the rich variety of forms to be seen in mint, the orchid, and the microscopic beauty of the grasses. Some buds produce only flowers, others a mixture of flowers and foliage; in some plants the sexes are separate, in others combined in one flower. With the production of the seed, the cycle nears completion, and the tiny embryo with its food reserve and protective coating speaks again, through its form and texture, of the parent plant which produced it.

Form, in plants or in the mind, is more than geometric shape. Rather, it is the essential expression of function; and from the time when primitive man began to trace figures in the sand, it is to the forms of earth that the artist has returned, like Anteus, for his strength. The camera has not, as some have claimed, displaced other representative arts. The photographs which follow, it seems to me, offer something quite different: a means and a discipline toward a vision of life at once old and fresh as rain.

PAUL B. SEARS

PREFACE

Between the world as seen by the naked eye and that visible through a microscope there lies a realm of form, texture, and color largely unknown to most people. Yet this remarkable universe can be explored with nothing more than a hand lens or pocket magnifier. In a lifetime one can explore only a few pathways through this middle-sized world of plants and animals.

The pictures on the following pages not only reveal beauty of structure but in many cases show how plants respond or adapt to their environment, not only during the lifetime of the individual plant but also over millions of years. These plant patterns, though rarely seen because of their small size, may provide students, designers, and others with new and exciting departures for creative expression.

W. M. H.

13

NOTES ON PLANT
CHARACTERISTICS

Leaves. Often the shape, size, margin, and arrangement of a leaf are all that is needed to identify a plant. Because certain groups of plants always have a typical leaf placement, the arrangement of the leaves on the stem is an important part of identification. Leaves are either alternate and arranged singly in spirals—or opposite—that is, paired. A few plants have whorled leaves, with three or more at the same height on the stem.

Usually, opposite or whorled leaves are easily recognized, but alternate leaves may present problems. If twig or stem growth is very slow, alternate leaves may be so crowded that they appear to be opposite or whorled. The solution is to look for stems growing normally on the plant; here it will be more obvious that the leaves occur singly.

Another problem in determining arrangement is that of whether or not a leaf is simple and one-bladed, or compound, with a number of leaflets. In some compound leaves, such as those of the horsechestnut, the usual seven leaflets radiate from the end of the leaf stem. The leaflets of most compound leaves, however, including those of hickory, ash, and walnut, have a different placement. These pinnate or "featherlike" leaves consist of a straight stem with lateral leaflets attached on both sides, and usually with an end or terminal leaflet at the tip. Leaf arrangement does not refer to the placement of the leaflets on the midrib, but only to the way in which the leaf itself, simple or compound, is attached to the woody axis of the plant. In broad-leaved trees and other woody plants, if one follows the leaf from tip to base, there will usually be found, except in the early spring, a bud where the leaf joins the twig.

Most broad-leaved trees are deciduous, bare in winter and leafing out again the next spring. By contrast, most needle-leaved trees—pines, spruces, firs—retain the leaves they developed the previous summer, and are "evergreen." This does not mean that these trees never lose their leaves, but only that the last season's leaves remain at least until the new ones emerge in spring. The leaves of most evergreens are shed after three to five years; in a few species, they may be retained much longer. Variations in leaf margins, shapes of apex and base, types of veining, and other features, are best learned when the leaves are collected and their identity determined with a tree manual or reliable handbook.

Perhaps the most fascinating thing about leaves is their dissimilarity: the fact that no two are exactly the same size and shape. This means that one must learn the range of variation of the different species. The tulip tree, for example, has leaves which are quite similar, one to the other, but the shapes of oak leaves are highly variable, both on the same tree and from one region to another.

Flowers. The word "flower" usually suggests large showy petals such as those of the rose, poppy, iris, lily, magnolia, and the hundreds of others with which man has surrounded himself. Plants in the wild often have small flowers, however; in trees, especially, these are often so small and inconspicuous as to pass unnoticed. Be that as it may, the beauties of their structure will reward anyone who examines them with a hand lens.

In many species of trees, the stamens are borne in separate flowers from the pistils, male and female on the same tree; such species are called *monoecious,* from two Greek words meaning in one house. In *dioecious* species, "two houses," the male flowers are borne on one tree, the female on another.

Fruits. A fruit, quite simply, is a ripened ovary containing one or more seeds. On page 66 is shown the pistil of a walnut tree; the lower portion is the ovary. It must now be emphasized that in nature there is the utmost variation of fruit types, just as there is in the flowers which precede them. It has been said that "Man, the observer and cataloguer, looks at nature and for convenience desires, imagines, and describes *uniformity.* Actually, there is infinite *variety;* between the two there is constant conflict." The fruit of pines and spruces is a cone, and the "flowers" which precede them have no ovaries; the seeds are borne on the surface of the scales.

The word "fruit" has many different meanings, and, perhaps unfortunately, everyone is sure that he knows exactly what the right one is. To give a technical meaning to such a common and loosely used word poses problems for the amateur seeking to understand the language of botanists. Quite often the type of fruit cannot be determined with confidence merely by looking at it, or even by dissecting it. One must watch while its precursor, the flower, slowly develops into the mature fruit.

Seeds. Perhaps the unequaled expression of the plant world is the seed. Each is like a miniature spaceship containing a new plant, the embryo, and a limited amount of food and water for a trip. In some plants, germination begins as soon as the seed lands in a suitable place, but in many others, it loses most of its water and the embryo sinks into a state of lethargy, requiring little oxygen and remaining dormant for months or even years. In temperate-climate plants, the seeds of many species must experience winter before they will germinate. This safeguards them from making false starts during unusually warm periods in the late autumn.

Buds. Buds are only conspicuous in early spring, yet new buds appear as the leaves grow from their developing twigs in May and June at the latitude of New York, and earlier farther south. These buds may be found in the axil or angle between the leaf and the twig, but it is not until late summer or early autumn that they are fully formed.

Since the buds of woody plants are present for most of the year and have conspicuous features of structure and color, their recognition is important. Buds are of two types: a bud may be *terminal,* on the end of the twig; or *lateral,* growing at some point along the side of the twig. Trees with terminal buds also have laterals, but in some groups, such as the birches, elms, and basswoods, no true terminal bud ever forms. As summer advances, there comes a time when length-growth slows and finally stops altogether. The slender tip of the twig then shrinks and dies back to the last well-formed lateral bud, now called the *false terminal* bud. The shriveled twig tip usually falls off leaving a minute round scar on the twig. A true terminal bud is generally larger than a false terminal and points straight ahead. Since buds occur in the leaf axils, except for the terminal bud, their arrangement on the twig is the same as that of the leaves.

Twigs. Significant twig features are type of pith, leaf scars, color, odor, and taste. When one slices a twig lengthwise with a sharp knife, most species show a homogeneous pith. Exceptions are the walnuts, including the butternut, which have crosswise partitions separating empty chambers, and the tupelos in which the solid pith shows cross-walls of a darker tissue.

Some time before autumn frosts, a special layer of loose, easily ruptured cells develops at the base of each leaf stem. Beneath this layer another layer of corky tissue forms next to the twig. It is not until the leaf falls off or is blown away that this corky layer, the leaf scar, appears on the twig. Then small patches or bundle scars mark the position of the sap-carrying and food translocating channels which passed from twig to leaf. The leaf scar with its bundle scars often looks like a tiny gargoyle's face (p. 31).

In some trees, the color of the twig is an important characteristic. For example, the golden color of a variety of white willow, the bright red of red-stemmed dogwood, the green of sassafras, and recognizable shades of greenish-brown on other kinds of twigs are examples which help in identification.

The odor and taste of a twig may provide a practical clue to its identity. Yellow and black birch have a wintergreen flavor, sassafras has a spicy taste, and the cherries taste of bitter almond. A few tropical species in Florida and other southern states have twigs which are very poisonous to chew. Also, be certain you can recognize poison-ivy, poison-oak, and poison-sumac before tasting any twig.

Bark. This is another important but variable feature used in tree recognition. As the young tree grows in diameter, more and more phloem layers are produced on the outer face of the cambium while new woody layers are added within (see ring patterns, pp. 108, 109). When the phloem layers outside the cambium accumulate sufficiently, an irregular layer or series of narrow curved patches of reactivated cells, the *cork cambium,* appears somewhere between the outside of the tree and the cambium. This development cuts off the outer phloem layers from the life of the tree, and they become dead outer bark in contrast to the living inner bark inside the cork cambium. It is important to observe in most trees the changing appearance of the bark, from youth to old age. The young bark of a white birch is brown, for example; it is only when the tree reaches a height of twenty feet or more that the brown bark is sloughed off revealing the typically white layers within. Beeches are an exception to this general rule of age coloration. (See bark patterns, pp. 98, 100.)

Growth. The growth habits of a plant often assist in its identity. The plant may creep along the ground or be bushy or treelike in form. Branch patterns and the shape of the crown often confirm recognition (pp. 94, 96). Typical crown shapes develop only in open-growing trees; in the forest, competition with other individuals greatly restricts crown shape. Here all trees tend to have tall straight trunks and small crowns—exactly what the forester desires. Trees which are grown in the open usually yield poor lumber, the many branches along the trunk appearing as knots when a log is sawed.

Habitat. Plants, like animals, tend to find certain environmental niches more suitable than others. There are quite recognizable plant societies associated with differences in available moisture, soil, and temperature. A good example is the bog society which develops in a creeping mat of sphagnum moss around the edges of shallow, poorly drained ponds. From a plane flying across Canada or the northern United States, one may see countless small lakes and ponds slowly filling with a bog society of sphagnum moss, Labrador tea, leatherleaf, pitcher plant, sheep-laurel, blueberries, and other plants. Behind them, forming the forest, are the black spruce and tamarack.

Spirals. Wherever one looks in the universe there are spirals: from the celestial to the sub-microscopic, from the giant spiral nebulae to the molecules of DNA in living protoplasm. Many of the pictures which follow show spiral structures of great beauty and variety. Shown among others are the twigs of three common trees: basswood, alder, and willow (page 29). Their buds and leaves, like those of other alternate-leaved plants, not only exhibit an over-all spiral pattern but each represents a different type of spiral.

Spirals have given rise to an interesting series of fractions. In determining them, two buds may be chosen, one exactly above the other. Beginning with the lower bud, an upward turn is described until the bud directly above the starting point is reached. This relationship between stem turns and bud count is expressed as a fraction, the numerator of which represents the number of whole turns necessary to arrive at the higher bud, the denominator the number of buds counted in that section of the spiral. Part of the series is $\frac{1}{2}$, $\frac{1}{3}$, $\frac{2}{5}$, $\frac{3}{8}$, $\frac{5}{13}$, $\frac{8}{21}$. . . .

Among trees and shrubs, the $\frac{1}{2}$ arrangement is characteristic of basswood and the elms, the $\frac{2}{5}$ of oaks, willows, and poplars. A $\frac{1}{3}$ arrangement is rare, but typical of alder. Dr. R. R. Hirt of the New York College of Forestry at Syracuse discovered that needle bundles in the white pine follow a $\frac{5}{13}$ arrangement. These higher fractions are not easy to determine because of the difficulty in choosing buds, leaves, or needle bundles one exactly above the other.

Wood Structure.   Perhaps in all of nature there are no more beautiful or significant patterns than those of the growth layers in trees. Seen in cross section on a stump or log, or in the end of a piece of wood, these ring patterns faithfully indicate the life history of the tree. In good years the rings are wide; in poor years, narrow. What makes a year, or, more properly, a growing season, good or poor? Trees, like all other plants, must have water, and the amount of water available to the roots is reflected in the ring width. But like other green plants, trees need light, as well; and trees growing under heavy shade have narrow rings even though they may have had plenty of water.

Since the simple sugars, the basic food of the tree, are made in the green leaves, anything that robs a tree of its leaves will reduce the amount of wood laid down. Defoliating insects and fire may have a definite effect on ring width. Temperature variations throughout the growing season normally affect ring width less than a scarcity of water and light. Exceptions are alpine trees which receive ample water and light; in this case, extreme temperature changes largely control their growth.

In places such as the arid Southwest, trees growing apart from one another on dry, well-drained slopes have ring patterns directly reflecting the amount of water they receive each year. Scientists at the Tree Ring Laboratory of the University of Arizona have constructed tree ring calendars beginning at the present time and extending back for hundreds of years. Knowing that the life history of trees is recorded in their rings, you may wish to try your hand at interpreting the stories told by the rings on pp. 108, 109, before reading their interpretations at the bottom of each page.

On pp. 112–117 are photographs of four kinds of wood as seen in cross section, made from thin sections and illuminated from behind. In each case, the center of the tree is some distance below the bottom of the picture, and the tree grew toward the top of the page. How trees add new growth each season is a mystery to many, including, it seems, to some lumberjacks. One of them was heard to remark that it did no harm to knock the bark off a tree because new rings kept forming at the center and these just pushed the old ones outward.

Actually, between the inner bark and the wood is the remarkable layer of cells called the *cambium*. During the growing season, these cells, by repeated divisions, form new bark on the outside and new wood upon that of the previous season. Trees grow in length only at their twig and root tips, therefore a nail driven into the bark of a tree six feet above the ground will remain at that height.

In woods of the temperate zones, there are usually visible differences in each ring between the wood formed at the beginning of the growing season and that laid down near its end. The earlywood is liable to be more porous and less dense than the latewood. Usually, this makes the earlywood light in color, the latewood darker. In oak, a so-called *ring-porous* wood (page 114), the earlywood consists of relatively large sap-conducting tubes which are seen as pores in cross section. The pores abruptly become much smaller in the latewood zone, and most of the latewood is dense, heavy, and strong. In the sycamore (page 116), the pores are relatively small and uniform in size throughout the ring. Such woods are called *diffuse-porous*.

Both the oak and the sycamore show conspicuous dark radial lines known as *wood rays,* common to all woods. In the oaks where the rays are especially large, they provide the beautiful silver grain seen on radially cut boards. Redwood (page 117), unlike the oak and sycamore, has no pores, instead being composed of long hollow fibrous cells.

WITCH-HOBBLE BUD $\times$ 10

Viburnum alnifolium Marsh.

The first two leaves of next year's growth are infolded and thickened in this scaleless bud. The vein pattern will be on the underside of the expanded leaf. Such scaleless or naked buds are common only to a few trees and shrubs.

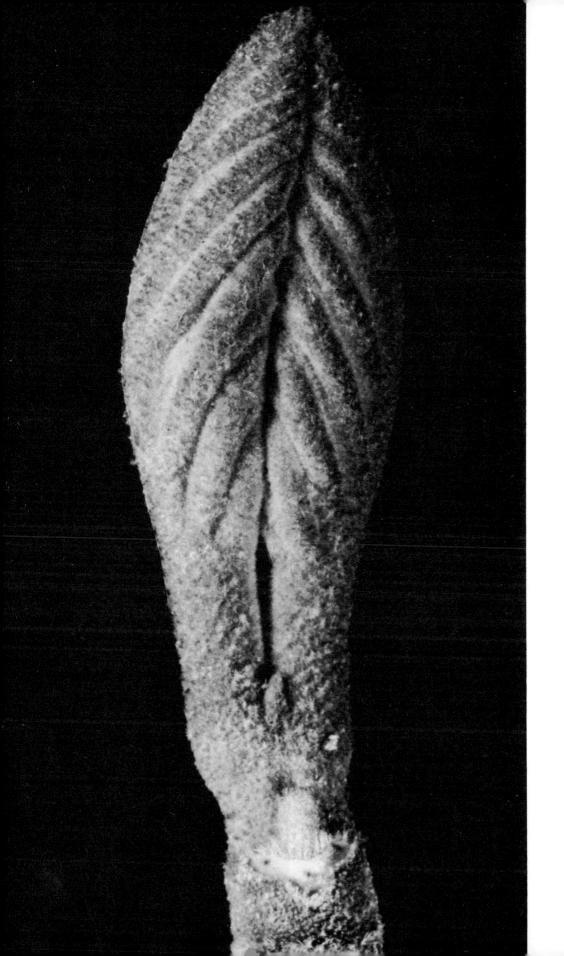

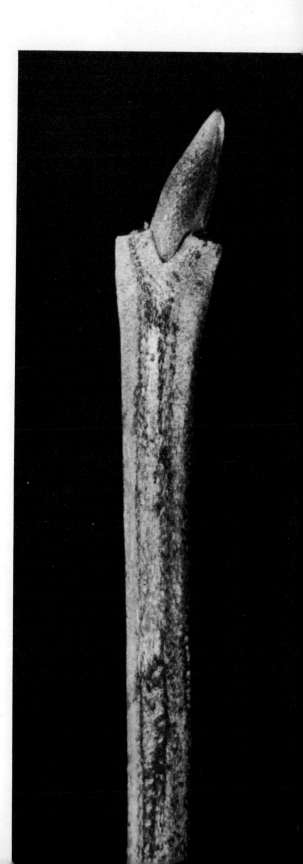

LEAF BUD AND FLOWER BUD OF FLOWERING DOGWOOD × 8

Cornus florida L.

In many trees, leaves and flowers emerge from the same bud; in the flowering dogwood they come from separate and dissimilar buds. The four scales of the flower bud expand into petal-shaped bracts. Some twenty small greenish flowers are borne in a flat-topped head in the center.

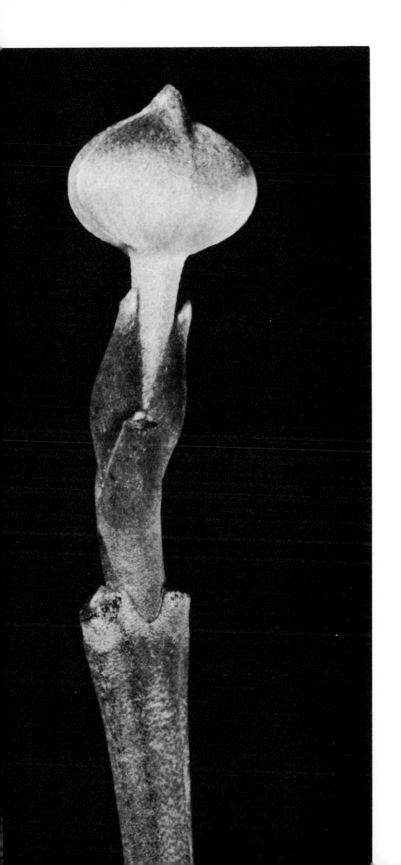

BUDS OF BLACK MAPLE $\times$ 15

Acer nigrum Michx.

The black maple is similar to the sugar maple, but the buds of the former are stouter and more hairy. The lens-shaped patches, called *lenticels*, allow air to pass into the tissues beneath the outer skin. Lenticels are found on all twigs.

WHITE ASH TWIGS
Fraxinus americana L.

The difference in the growth rate of two twigs growing near each other is often remarkable. As the buds open in the spring, the scales curl back and fall off, leaving narrow scars. Each group of scars indicates the beginning of a year's new growth. The twig on the left grew near the outside of the crown where it got plenty of light; the seven-year-old dwarf on the right grew in the shade.

SPIRAL BUDS ON TWIGS OF BASSWOOD, ALDER, AND WILLOW × 1½

Tilia americana L., *Alnus rugosa* (Du Roi) Spreng., *Salix discolor* Muhl.

In determining the spiral fraction for the basswood twig at the left, one turn about the stem includes two buds; the resulting fraction is ½. For the alder, three buds are counted: ⅓. In the case of the willow, five buds are counted, but two complete turns are necessary to go from one starting bud to another. The fraction is ⅖.

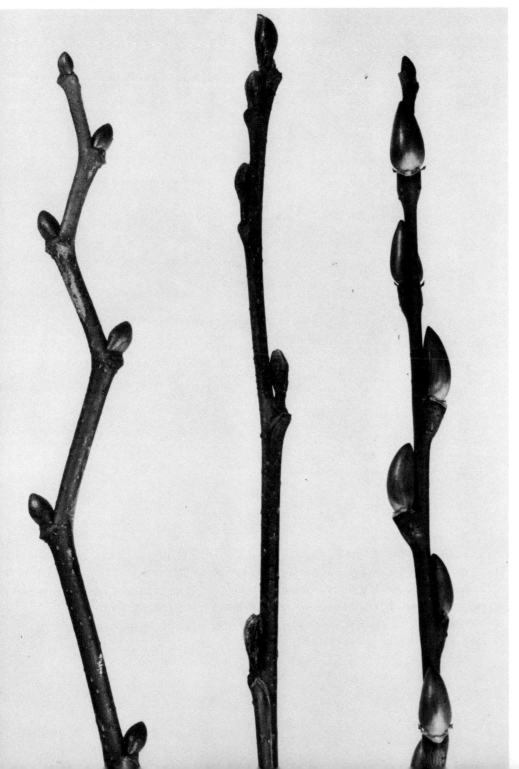

TWIGS OF BLACK WALNUT AND BUTTERNUT × 4

Juglans nigra L., *Juglans cinerea* L.

These two American trees are well-known for both their fruit and beautiful cabinet wood. In the walnuts shown here, the bundle scars are in horseshoe-shaped groups, making each leaf scar look like a tiny horse's face.

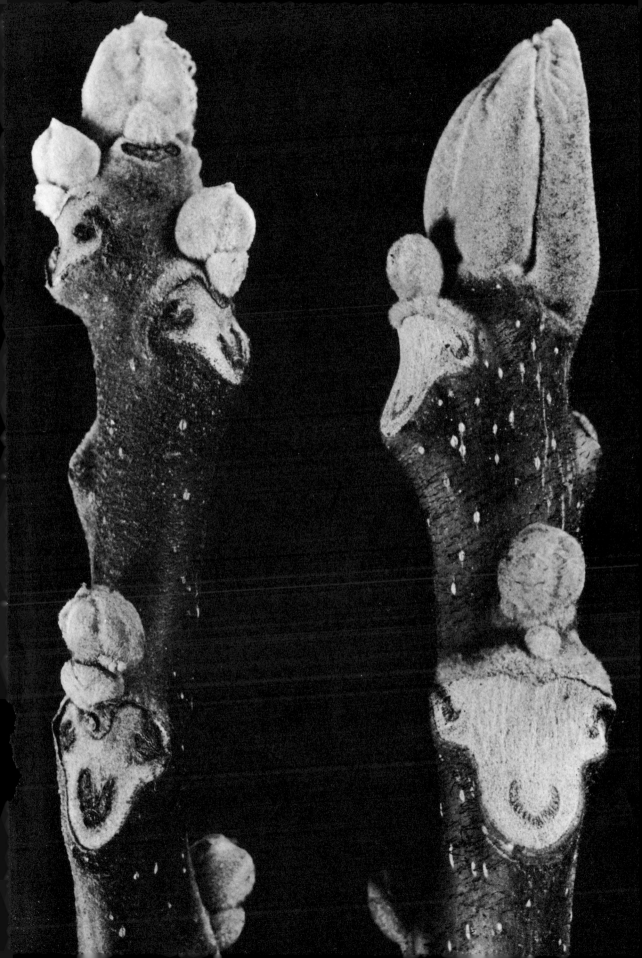

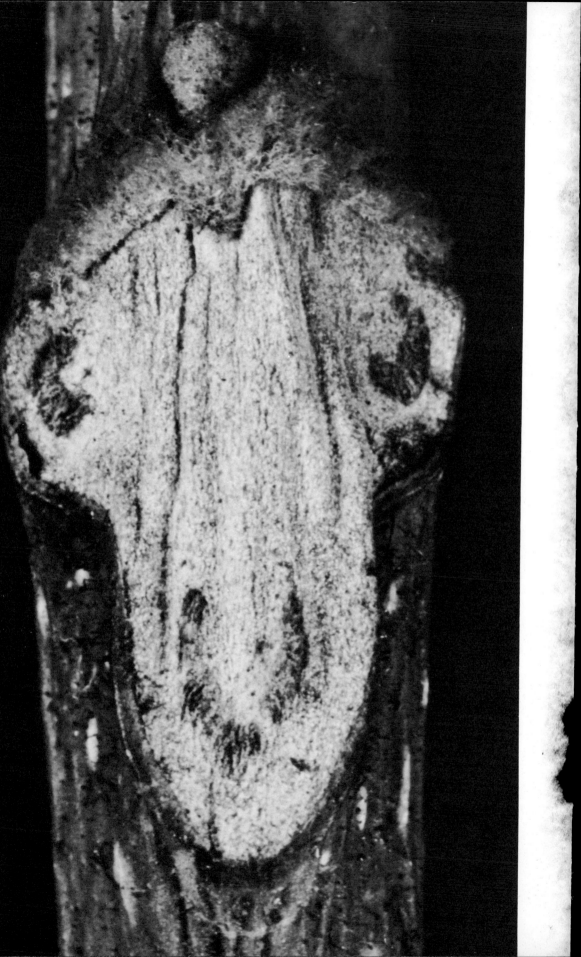

LEAF SCAR OF BUTTERNUT × 12
Juglans cinerea L.

Notice that the face has hair over its "forehead." This differentiates it from the black walnut. The entire surface of the leaf scar is covered by a corky layer that prevents evaporation of water from the twig.

RHODODENDRON BUD × 3¼
Rhododendron maximum L.

The flower bud shown here is much larger than a leaf bud. By counting flower buds the previous summer you can estimate the amount of flowering for the next spring.

OPENING BUDS OF LILAC × 8

Syringa vulgaris L.

The opening green bud scales of the lilacs are among the first signs of spring. From day to day the inner scales look more and more like leaves as they expand. These bud scales seem to have evolved from blades of the lilac leaves.

 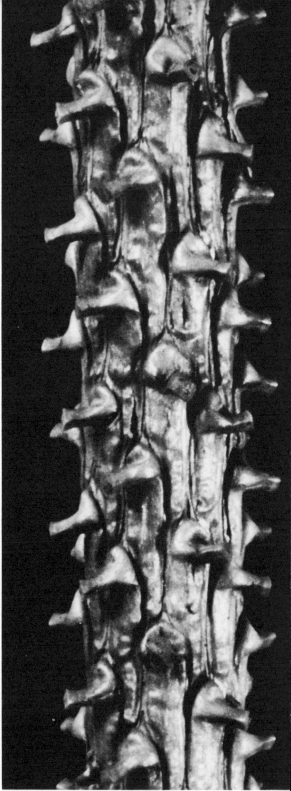

TWIGS OF FIR AND SPRUCE × 10
Abies sp. and *Picea* sp.
One of the best ways to distinguish firs from spruces is by the bare twigs from which the leaves or needles have fallen. In the firs, including the balsam fir, a circular scar marks the place of leaf attachment. Spruce needles grow from small peglike projections of the twig itself.

SWEETGUM TWIG × 3

Liquidambar styraciflua L.

The sweetgum tree often has corky ridges on its twigs. Sometimes growth from the terminal bud of a tree becomes dwarfed, and a lateral bud continues normal growth.

OPENING BUD OF AMERICAN BEECH × 4
Fagus grandifolia Ehrh.

Some of the most beautiful patterns in plants are displayed by leaves as they emerge from the buds. Buds never "burst," however; they open slowly over periods of hours or days. By speeding up growth from 500 to 5,000 times with a time-lapse camera some remarkable motion picture footage has been produced of opening buds.

WHISTLING-PINE FOLIAGE × 3½
Casuarina equisetifolia L.

Actually belonging to the broad-leaved group of trees, the name may come from the sound of the wind sweeping through the tree's crown of slender branches. The leaves are nothing more than tiny scales, and the branches themselves are green and synthesize food sugars for the tree. Whistling-pine comes from Australia and has been widely planted throughout the warmer parts of the world.

PORT-ORFORD-CEDAR × 10

Chamaecyparis lawsoniana (A. Murr.) Parl.

The fanlike branchlets of this large Pacific Coast tree bear innumerable tiny, paired, scalelike leaves. Some viewers find in the white markings on the leaves the cross of St. Andrew.

DAWN REDWOOD FOLIAGE × 1½

Metasequoia glyptostroboides Hu and Cheng

The dawn redwood is perhaps the most exciting botanical discovery of this century. Found in 1941 in a remote province in China, it was supposed to have become extinct twenty million years ago. Seeds were brought out, and the tree was established in several countries. It can be easily propagated by cuttings and is now available from many sources.

LEAVES OF TAMARACK × 7
Larix laricina (Du Roi) K. Koch
The larches are conifers which lose their leaves in autumn. The leaves on the first year's growth are borne singly in spirals. By the end of the season, a number of stubby side buds develop and from these the leaves grow for several years thereafter in false compact whorls as shown.

BLUE SPRUCE NEEDLES
× 3
Picea pungens Engelm.
Great variation can be found in the color of individual trees of the Colorado blue spruce. Seeds from one wild-growing tree will produce off-spring varying in color from many shades of green to silver.

NEEDLES OF WHITE PINE × 3
Pinus strobus L.
Pines are recognized by their needles, which occur in bundles. The five needles of the white pine shown are fitted together to form a cylinder. To the Iroquois Indian tribes the five needles bound together symbolize the five nations in the league.

NIKKO FIR × 3
Abies homolepis Sieb. and Zucc.
This Oriental species with its stiff, spirally arranged leaves is planted as
an ornamental tree in the United States.

Each leaf of this plant is a study in radial symmetry.

NEW LEAVES OF APPLE $\times$ 1½
Malus pumila Mill.
This shaded apple twig grew very slowly. By counting the transverse groups of bud scars, one can calculate its probable age.

TULIPTREE LEAF
Liriodendron tulipifera L.

There are only two species of the *Liriodendron* in the world; one is in eastern China, and the other is an important timber tree of the eastern United States. It is supposed that at one time, before the Rocky Mountains rose, the two species were one, ranging across the Aleutian Bridge into Asia.

VEIN PATTERN TULIPTREE LEAF × 3
Liriodendron tulipifera L.

Veins are the pipe lines of a leaf. The smallest veinlet can be traced back to the central complex or midrib of the leaf. Through veins a continuous supply of water and dissolved minerals flows into the leaf, and sugars and other food materials made by the leaf are carried back into the stem and growing parts of the tree.

SWEETGUM LEAF
Liquidambar styraciflua L.

Sweetgum is an important southern veneer-producing tree; in the north, it is valued for its brilliant autumn leaves. When cuts are made in the bark, a balsamic resin exudes and hardens into droplets. Storax used in the making of perfume can be extracted from the resin.

PARALLEL VEIN PATTERN OF A CORN LEAF
Zea mays L.

Seed plants are divided into two broad groups. Monocotyledons such as corn, grasses, and many others, have leaves with parallel veins; the other group, dicotyledons, have leaves with branching veins which form a complex network. (See tuliptree, p. 50 and sweetgum, p. 52.)

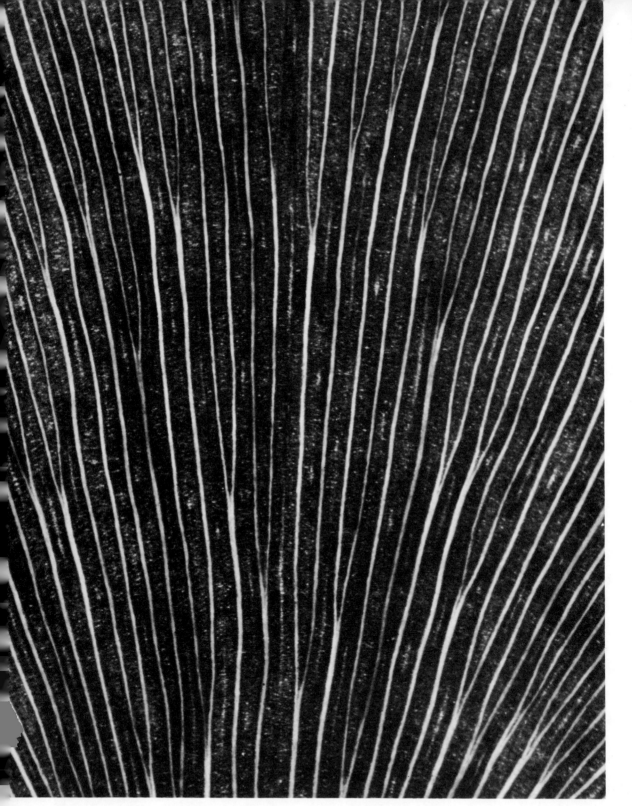

VEIN PATTERN OF A GINKGO LEAF $\times$ 8

Ginkgo biloba L.

This is the vein pattern of one of the most ancient trees in the world. Each vein always branches into two others, and they in turn divide in the same way. The ginkgo with its fan-shaped leaves belongs to the primitive gymnosperms which also include the conifers.

WAYFARING-TREE LEAF VEINS $\times$ 3

Viburnum lantana L.

This is another example of net venation; the pattern is reinforced by the heavy covering of hair (pubescence) on the undersurface of the leaf.

SKELETONIZED BEAN LEAF × 5

Phaseolus sp.

Compared to the soft green tissues between them, the veins of leaves are woody, consisting of water-conducting tubes. Leaf-eating insects tend to eat out the softer tissues and leave the veins relatively untouched.

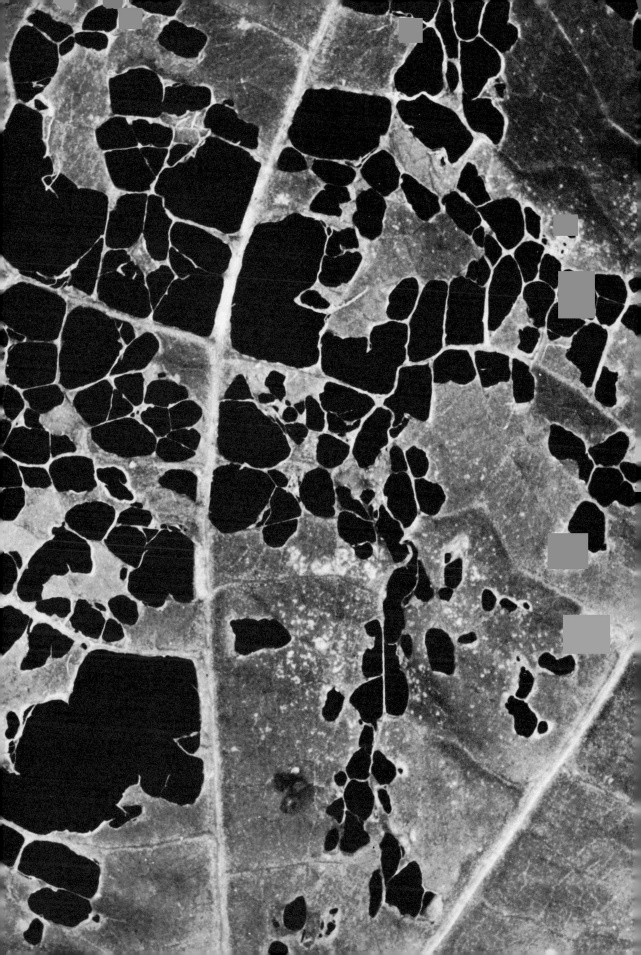

ONION AND BEAN SEEDLINGS GROWING TOWARD LIGHT
Allium sp. and *Phaseolus* sp.

Indoor plants reach toward a window or other source of light. Outdoors on a very hot sunny day, the leaves of beans and some other plants slowly turn and present their

edges to the sun. Later in the afternoon when sunlight is less intense, the leaves move back to a position facing the sky.

ALOE
Aloe sp.

These plants of the lily family are widely distributed in dry parts of the earth, especially in Southern Africa. They are now widely planted throughout the warmer parts of the world as ornamentals and in cooler regions as house plants.

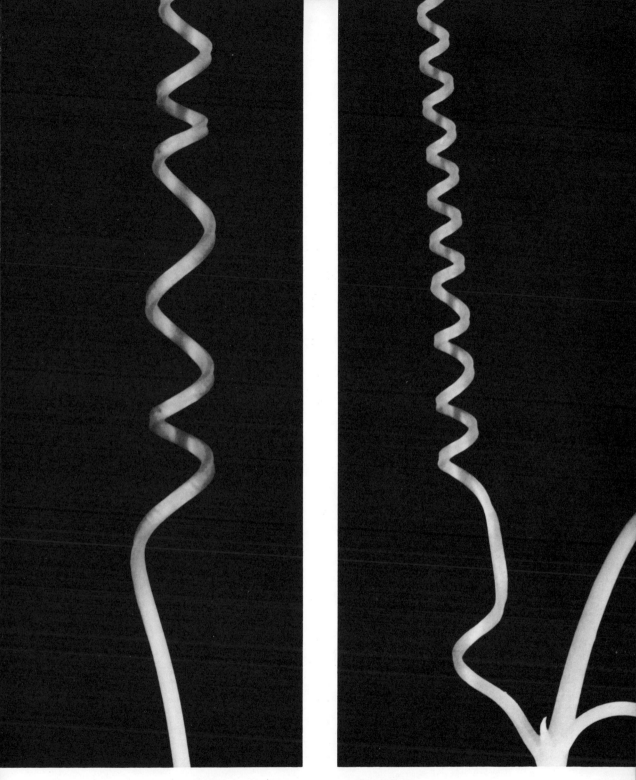

TENDRILS OF WILD CUCUMBER × 5

Echinocystis lobata (Michx.) T. and G.

Some of the most beautiful spirals of nature are displayed by the tendrils of certain plants. The long slender tendrils of this wild cucumber make sweeping circular motions, and when the sensitive tip touches a support it encircles it in about a minute. The tendril then shortens itself by forming a spiral and draws the plant over to the support.

POLLEN GALAXY: MALE FLOWERING CONES OF JACK PINE × 3

Pinus banksiana Lamb.

The amount of pollen discharged from even a single cluster of cones must be numbered in the billions. A light breeze is enough to carry pollen a long way through a forest, and the chances of pollen from the male cones of a tree reaching the female cones of another tree are very good.

FEMALE FLOWERING CONES OF A PINE × 3

Pinus sp.

Though the young cones may be bright red they are too small to be seen easily. Little growth occurs the first season. The next spring the cones in most species turn over and become pendent, and the rate of growth accelerates. In the largest-coned pines, from less than an inch, cones two feet long develop the second season.

MALE FLOWERING CONES OF EASTERN HEMLOCK × 10
Tsuga canadensis (L.) Carr.

The hemlocks are graceful, ornamental trees of moist, shady places. Hemlock tea brewed from the "needles" was used to treat the malnutritional disease, scurvy. The "poison-hemlock" mentioned in ancient times has no connection at all with this tree, but is a relatively rare herbaceous plant.

BUD OF ICELAND POPPY × 6

Papaver nudicaule L.

These poppies are now widely planted in gardens throughout the cooler parts of the world. See also p. 90.

FEMALE FLOWER OF ENGLISH WALNUT × 8

Juglans regia L.

Because tree flowers are usually small and without showy or colorful petals, they go unseen. The large feathery stigma at the top of the walnut flower is adapted for trapping wind-borne pollen.

BACHELOR'S-BUTTON BUD × 6

Centaurea sp.

Like the dandelion, this plant belongs to the vast composite group of plants in which each "flower" is a compact head of many flowers. The bud scales illustrate a spiral pattern.

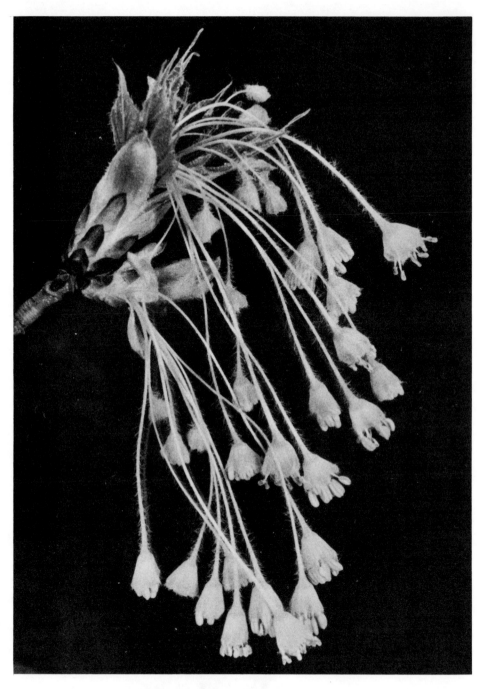

SUGAR MAPLE FLOWERS × 1¾

Acer saccharum Marsh.

In some trees flowers appear each spring, but in others they are borne at several-year intervals. This is the way of the sugar maple; when flowering does occur, a tree often bears so heavily that for a few days it seems, at a distance, to be covered with a yellow mist. Flowering lasts but a few days and the emerging leaves soon cover the tree with a new mantle of fresh green.

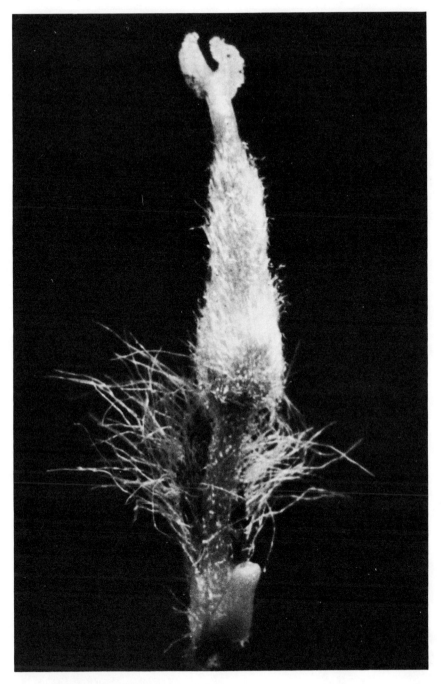

SINGLE FEMALE FLOWER OF A WILLOW $\times$ 38
Salix sp.

When one thinks of willows it is usually the furry catkins that are visualized. Each catkin consists of several hundred of these tiny flowers packed tightly together along a central axis; the males and females on separate trees.

TORCH LILY × 3

Kniphofia sp. or *Tritoma* sp.

Borne on a tall stem, this cluster of orange or yellow flowers is a common feature of many gardens.

TEASEL $\times$ 3

Dipsacus sylvestris Huds.

The teasels, introduced from Europe, have an interesting history. For centuries the bristly fruiting heads of a species closely related to the one illustrated here have been used to comb up or tease a hairy layer or nap on wool cloth. Originally brought to this country for this purpose, these plants now are usually considered weeds.

BULL THISTLE $\times$ 4

Cirsium pumilum (Nutt.) Spreng.

The flowering head consists of one hundred or more tiny flowers packed tightly together. Were it not for this weed's formidable spines and territorial ambitions, it might be cultivated in many gardens.

CONE OF PONDEROSA PINE $\times$ 1½

Pinus ponderosa Laws.

Cones used for decoration have usually opened. To observe a closed cone, simply place it in water; within an hour or two the scales close. On dry sunny days after a cone reaches maturity the scales open releasing winged seeds; in rainy weather, poor for "flying," the scales remain closed.

PASSION-FLOWER $\times$ 3

Passiflora sp.

The first Spaniards in South America connected the flower's structure with the signs of the crucifixion: The three upper parts of the pistil became the three nails, the five stamens were the five wounds, surrounded by a crown of thorns. The ten "petals" represented the ten apostles at the crucifixion.

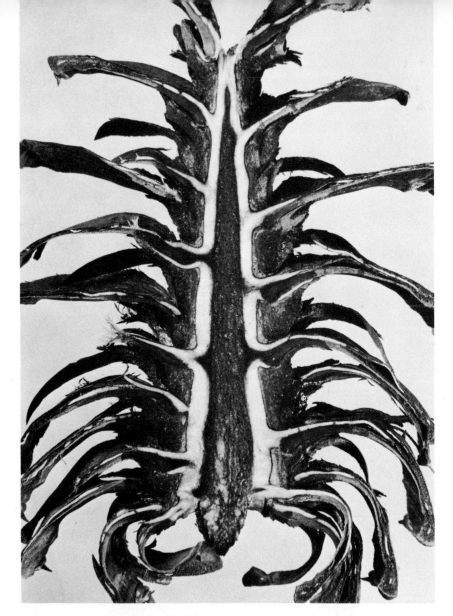

CONE OF PONDEROSA PINE (lengthwise section) × 2

Pinus ponderosa Laws.

The opening and closing mechanism of the scales of a pine cone is remarkable. Each scale in section shows a white upper band of tissue and a brownish lower band. The white band shrinks very little when the cone dries out; the lower band may shrink from 20 to 30 per cent or more. This shrinkage causes the scale to curve away from the cone axis and exposes the seeds.

WEATHERED CONE SCALES OF COULTER PINE × 2

Pinus coulteri D. Don

These cone scales illustrate one of the many spiral patterns found in nature. The netlike texture of most of the scales was produced over several years by weathering as the cones lay on the ground.

CONE OF DOUGLAS-FIR × 2½

Pseudotsuga menziesii (Mirb.) Franco

This species is the most important single timber producer in the United States and is also widely planted as an ornamental. The two-lobed bracts, each with a central spine or tail, make its cone easy to recognize.

CONE OF GIANT SEQUOIA × 2½

Sequoia gigantea (Lindl.) Decne.

The giant sequoia or big-tree of the Sierra Nevada Mountains in California is one of the world's most famous and awe-inspiring trees. Even medium-sized trees are 75 feet around at the base. With the light from a whitely overcast sky, the great trunks glow a rosy red.

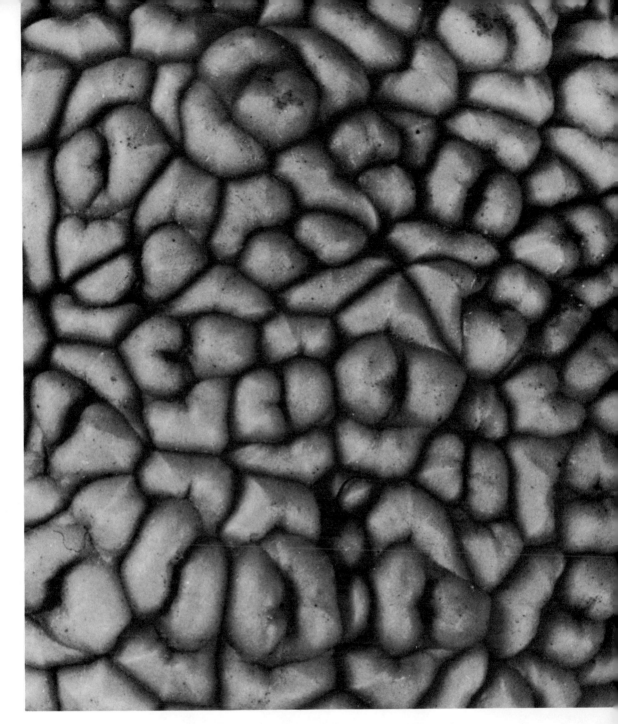

FRUIT SURFACE OF OSAGE-ORANGE × 6

Maclura pomifera (Raf.) Schneid.

The green, ball-shaped fruit with its bitter milky sap is about 4 inches in diameter and has a strangely sculptured surface unlike that of any other native species.

CONE SCALES OF BLUE SPRUCE × 7

Picea pungens Engelm.

Blue spruce, native to the Rocky Mountains, has now become one of the commonest and most widely planted ornamentals of North America. The cones are about 3½ inches long; the spiral arrangement of the scales is typical of many conifers.

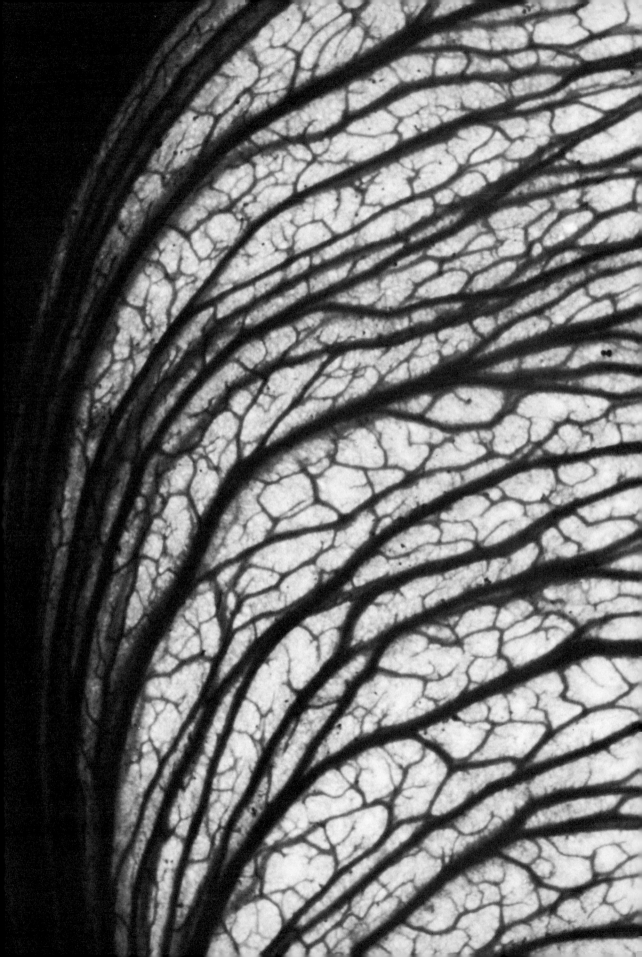

NORTHERN RED OAK ACORN × 6

Quercus rubra L.

This oak is one of our important forest trees. Even at natural size the
acorn is the largest of those in northeastern red oaks.

WING VEINS IN SILVER MAPLE × 12

Acer saccharinum L.

The winged fruits of the maples are well adapted for traveling by air.
Maple "keys" have been seen lofted by 60 mile-per-hour winds, spinning
along 150 feet above the ground. The vein framework of the wing suggests
an effective aeronautical design.

CHESTNUTS IN BUR × 3
Castanea dentata (Marsh.) Borkh.

The valuable American chestnut tree has been all but wiped out by a fungous disease, the chestnut blight, brought from Asia at the turn of the century. Asiatic chestnut trees are somewhat resistant to the fungus, and it is hoped that hybrids between our native tree and the Chinese chestnut may be disease-resistant and also possess the desirable qualities of the American chestnut.

CHESTNUT BUR SPINES × 7
Castanea dentata (Marsh.) Borkh.

No mammal can get at a chestnut until the frost opens its spiny husk. Beneath the spines is a hard horny layer, and inside of that a thick blanket of velvet. The seed itself is enclosed in a leathery case.

FLOWERING DOGWOOD FRUIT CLUSTER × 6

Cornus florida L.

Six of the flowers have developed into bright red fruits. Those that aborted may still be seen attached to the floral disk.

OPENED POD OF LUPINE × 5
Lupinus sp.

As lupine pods dry, they twist; this may cause the seeds to spring away from the parent plant. Blue lupines by the thousands mark high mountain slopes of the West. Annual and perennial species in several colors are garden favorites as well.

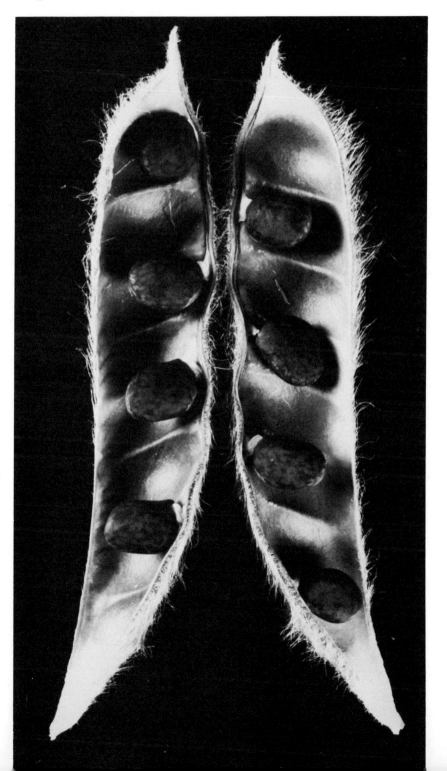

ELDERBERRY STEMS × 3

Sambucus canadensis L.

This pattern remains after birds have picked off the last elderberries from a cluster of two hundred or more.

FRUIT CAPSULE OF ORIENTAL POPPY $\times$ 6

Papaver orientale L.

The radial pattern of the stigma on the top of the fruit capsule provides an unusual design.

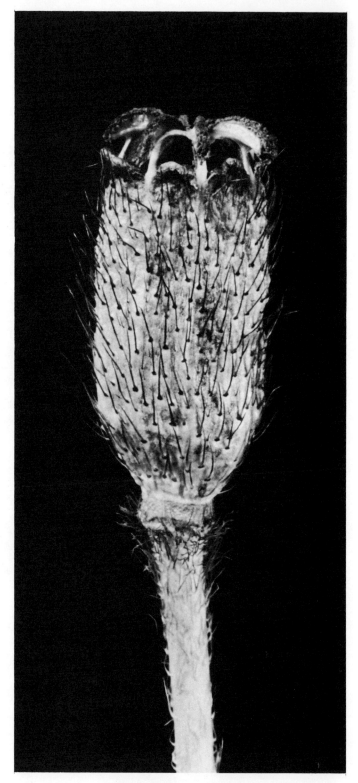

FRUIT CAPSULE OF
ICELAND POPPY × 8
Papaver nudicaule L.

When the wind blows hard or an animal brushes against the long stiff stem, some of the minute seeds are thrown out of the pores or openings on the top of the capsule.

STORKSBILL FRUIT
× 5 AND × 10
Erodium sp.

This is one of the most remarkable structures in nature. The seed is contained in a "gimlet" that burrows into the ground. When wet, the gimlet is straight; as it dries, it begins to twist, raising the boring end at an angle. Every change of moisture results in motion. The bristles help to anchor the drill tip.

DANDELION GONE
TO SEED × 3
Taraxacum sp.
Each fruit, or "seed," has
a parachute capable of car-
rying it for long distances.

COCKLEBUR × 5
Xanthium sp.
The hard, stiff, hooked
spines of the cocklebur
make it efficient in "hitch-
ing" rides on passing animals, including man.

AMERICAN ELM (winter)
Ulmus americana L.

These admired shade trees are being cut and burned by the thousands as they are killed by the Dutch elm disease, caused by a fungus carried on bark beetles which were brought from Europe in a shipment of veneer logs. Trees such as this magnificent specimen, twelve feet in circumference at breast height, may soon be only a memory.

AMERICAN ELM (summer)
Ulmus americana L.
Trees growing together in the forest cannot develop their typical crown shape.
Only in the open without competing neighbors do they show their distinctive form.

WHITE OAK (winter)
Quercus alba L.

Large, perfectly formed, open-grown trees are rare. This old white oak is nearly fifteen feet in circumference.

WHITE OAK (summer)

Quercus alba L.

Long life, five centuries or more, and durable wood have made oaks greatly respected by man. Since earliest times, ancient oaks have sheltered primitive altars; many of the most famous historical trees are oaks.

WHITE OAK BARK
Quercus alba L.
The bark patterns of most
trees change greatly from
youth to old age, yet each design is intriguing. This is an
old tree.

WHITE ASH BARK
Fraxinus americana L.
One sees in bark patterns a
similarity to the landscape
with its hills and valleys.
Here the pattern is of dia-
mond-shaped valleys bounded
by a network of flat ridges.

RED OAK BARK
Quercus rubra L.

In colonial days, tannin was a valuable product extracted from oak bark and used in producing leather from raw skins. Today quebracho wood from South America provides much of the commercial tannin used in the United States.

DATE PALM TREE
Phoenix canariensis Hort.

As with other palms, the outer surface of the stem is roughened where the leaves once grew.

ROOT SYSTEM OF BEAN × 3
Phaseolus vulgaris L.

From a long, fast-growing taproot, lateral roots emerge. Behind each root tip is a zone of numerous root hairs which absorb water and minerals from the soil.

PALM TREE FIBER
Livistona chinensis R. Br.

As the leaf bases weather, layers of interlacing fibers separate and fall off. Photographed against the sun, varied patterns appear in silhouette.

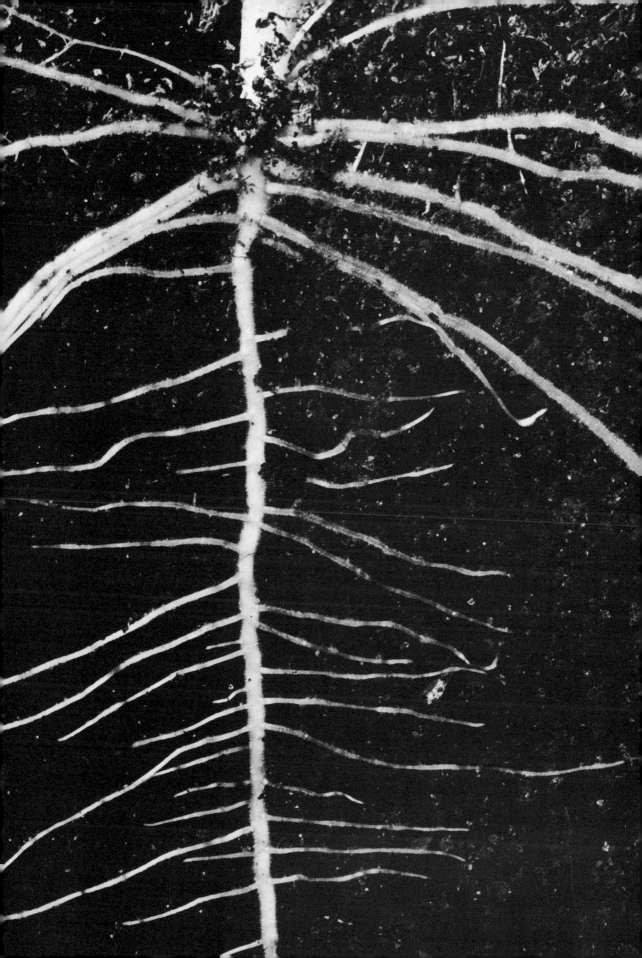

FIG TREE ROOTS
Ficus elastica Nois

Trees have extensive root systems extending down and outward to about the same distance from the trunk as the
branch tips overhead. Here, however, the roots lie on the
surface and look much like a river system or a collection
of bones.

SCREW-PINE AIR ROOTS

Pandanus utilis Bory

There is nothing pinelike about this tropical tree with aerial roots that grow down from the lower trunk to the ground. Its name may have derived from its cone-shaped fruit.

ROOT OF COTTONWOOD TREE
Populus deltoides Bartr.

This horizontal root grew among smooth, water-washed pebbles and larger stones on the shore of Lake Ontario. Perhaps the tree was washed out during a storm, and the broken root was tumbled in the surf until the bark was scoured away and the surface of the wood achieved its silky texture.

CROSS SECTION OF HEMLOCK TREE × ¾

Tsuga canadensis (L.) Carr.

For 75 years this tree grew very slowly under heavy shade. Then the surrounding trees were cut, and suddenly the tree had more than adequate light. The tree's response was remarkable; the rings are ten times the width of those formed before the tree was liberated.

TREE RINGS OF SOUTHERN PINE
Pinus sp.

The history of a tree is recorded in its growth rings. The tree on the left was probably enveloped by a fire which burned its needles. Growth faltered and then recovered, as indicated by the rings of normal width toward the top of the picture.

CROSS SECTION OF LAMINATED BEAM

A modern architectural use of wood is the laminated beam. Each piece or laminate has its own distinctive ring pattern.

WOOD GRAIN PATTERN IN OAK
Quercus sp.

From this oak railroad tie we can see how the growth layers of a branch merged with those of the main trunk. A knot is simply an embedded branch, seen here in cross section.

CROSS SECTION OF BUR OAK WOOD

Quercus macrocarpa Michx.

The width of the porous earlywood in each ring of this white oak varies
little from one ring to the next. The latewood varies markedly; the wider
the rings, the more there is of the heavy, strong, latewood.

CROSS SECTION OF PIN OAK WOOD $\times$ 8

Quercus palustris Muenchh.

This pin oak tree grew much faster than the bur oak. The latewood pores,
though small and few in number, are readily visible. This is a feature of
wood in the red oak group.

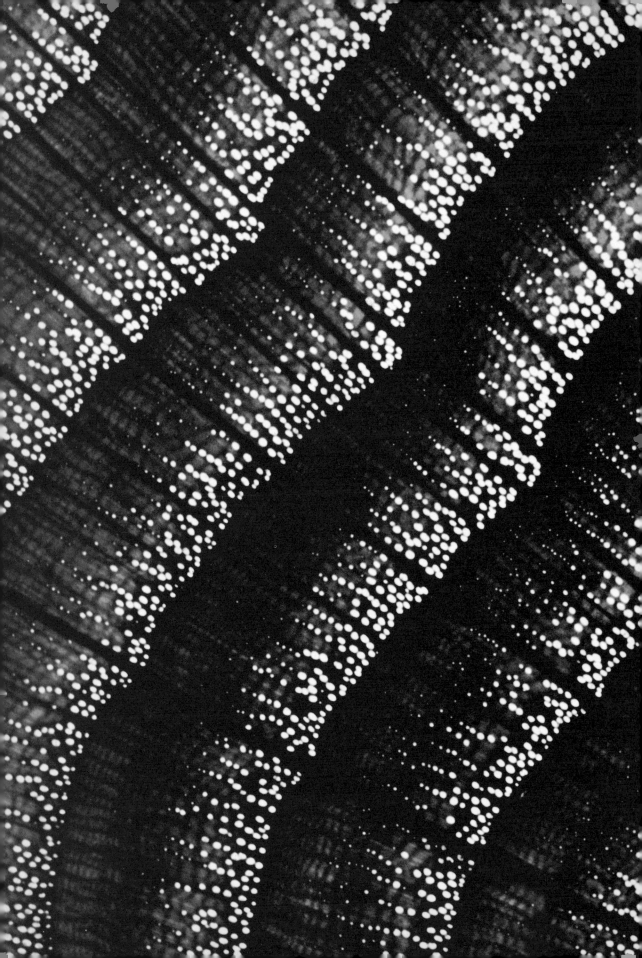

CROSS SECTION OF SYCAMORE WOOD × 5

Platanus occidentalis L.

Unlike the oak, the sap-conducting tubes of sycamore are about the same size throughout the ring; they are small compared to those in the earlywood of the oaks.

CROSS SECTION OF REDWOOD WOOD × 5

Sequoia sempervirens (D. Don) Endl.

Redwood, like all other conifers, has no specialized sap-conducting tubes. These primitive woods consist mainly of long hollow, closely-packed tracheids or fibers so small that they do not show at this magnification. The extremely narrow rings characterize old, slowly growing trees.

BURNED WOOD SURFACE

One might take this to be a photograph of the ruins of an ancient cathedral. This is a piece of plywood used in a fire test. Large wooden beams are more fire resistant than usually supposed, the first-formed charcoal insulating the wood underneath.

WOOD DECAY $\times$ 2

The phrase ''slow fire of decay'' has some truth, both from the standpoint of appearance and the end products of the two processes—carbon dioxide and water.

CORKY TWIGS OF WINGED EUONYMUS (SPINDLE-TREE) $\times$ 2
Euonymus alatus (Thunb.) Sieb.
In this species the twigs have a wide thin corky wing on each side particularly conspicuous in winter when the shrub is bare of leaves. Another species in this group is called burning-bush, because of its red autumn foliage.

NOTES ON THE PHOTOGRAPHIC TECHNIQUES

The art of discovering, selecting, and posing small plant parts showing beautiful and unusual patterns must precede capturing them on film. Having found something worth photographing, one must decide how to light it, what kind of background is best, and how much to reduce or magnify its size on film and in the final enlarged print.

Several of the prints in this book were made from negatives taken thirty years ago using one of the early 35 mm. cameras with a sliding, focusing, copying attachment. But most of them were made with a modern single lens reflex 35 mm. camera with extension tubes, or bellows attachment. Exceptions are the photos of deciduous trees in summer and winter taken with a twin lens $2\frac{1}{4} \times 2\frac{1}{4}$ format camera. For distant scenes, the larger the negative the better to produce the greatest of detail and sharpness in the final enlargement.

All of the small objects chosen were posed and photographed indoors using a more or less standard lighting arrangement of two photo floods (a No. 1 and a No. 2) from 1 to 2 feet on either side of the object, and at a vertical angle of about 45°. Although the object may be supported on a piece of glass with the white or black background several inches below it, unwanted reflections may register on the film, especially when using black. A piece of paper makes a suitable white background, but a good black was found difficult to achieve until someone suggested using black velvet, which proved excellent. When an object is photographed against white, unequal lighting produces a slight shadow on one side and gives a desirable feeling of depth or roundness. If the same lighting is used with a black background, one loses the shaded side altogether; therefore the lighting from both sides should be nearly equal.

Most small objects are photographed at one-fourth to three times natural size on 35 mm. film and then enlarged about ten times in the finished print. In this way, one uses the camera and enlarger together as a kind of low-power microscope, and unexpected details of structure and pattern are revealed. To capture the ultimate in detail, the lens diaphragm should not be closed more than about half-way. However, to achieve maximum depth of field, the diaphragm should be stopped down as far as it will go, and often this seems to be the most important of the two factors. Finally, although an exposure meter can be used, careful notes of trial exposures and the results obtained will prove invaluable, and when extension tubes separate lens from camera, exposure time must be increased.

As to choice of film, fine grain is needed and this has meant using a slow emulsion. Presently, several of the faster films have greatly improved grain structure so that speed need not be sacrificed. However, since time exposures are used, film speed is of little consequence. The important thing is to choose a good film and developer and then stay with them, learning all you can about their capabilities. Among photographers, in spite of the availability of suitable cameras and lenses the macro-field of plants and animals has hardly been explored. It offers great rewards for those with imagination.

LIST OF ILLUSTRATIONS